THE ONE MINUTE GRATITUDE JOURNAL FOR MOMS

A SIMPLE JOURNAL TO INCREASE GRATITUDE AND HAPPINESS

This Journal belongs to:

_____

ISBN: 978-1-952358-23-4

Gratitude

Gratitude is a feeling of appreciation for what one has. It is a feeling of thankfulness for the blessings we have received. Cultivating an attitude of gratitude yields many benefits: physical, mental and spiritual. Feeling gratitude in the present moment makes you happier and more relaxed, and improves your overall health and well-being.

With an eye made quiet by the power of harmony, and the deep power of joy,
we see into the life of things.
~ William Wordsworth

Gratitude doesn't just have to be about the big things. It can also be for small, everyday events. You can be thankful for simple things such as enjoying a movie or just talking to an old friend for the first time in a long while. There is always something that you can be grateful for in your life. It is all about appreciating the things around you rather than taking them all for granted.

Write down three to five things that you are grateful for each day. You will not only feel good as you write them down, but you will experience gratitude during the day as well. A person experiencing gratitude feels a sense of joy and abundance in their life. They also feel more connected with other people and have increased energy.

Gratitude should always be expressed in the present tense and is more powerful when combined with the perceived benefit so that an emotional connection is made. Instead of writing, *"I am grateful for my health and well-being,"* it is better to write, *"I am grateful for my health and well-being and it makes me feel great."*

No duty is more urgent than that of returning thanks.
~ James Allen

One of the healthiest and most positive things we can do in our lives is to express our gratitude to the people around us. Tell someone how much you appreciate them. Tell someone that something they did mattered to you. When people make an impact, let them know. We are usually too quick to point out people's faults and ways in which they have wronged us, while slow to bestow recognition for good deeds and favors.

If someone makes you feel good, make them feel good too. By expressing our gratitude to others, we are making the world a better place and encouraging the things that we want to see more of. Say, *"Thank you."* Make a difference. Seek out the best in people and when you find it, say something about it.

A gentle word, a kind look, a good-natured smile can work wonders and accomplish miracles.
~ William Hazlitt

Write down something amazing that happened in this journal every day. More amazing things will come into your life when you notice these and are appreciative for them.

Gratitude makes us more optimistic and compassionate. True happiness lies within us. By keeping a record of your gratitude in a journal, you will store positive energy, gain clarity in your life, and have greater control of your thoughts and emotions.

Each day, write down three to five things that you are grateful for in this journal and turn your ordinary moments into blessings.

It is never too late to be what you might have been.

~ George Eliot

Find ecstasy in life; the mere sense of living is joy enough.
— Emily Dickinson

Day: _____   Date: __/__/___

1. Today I am *Grateful* for:

_____
_____
_____
_____
_____
_____

2. Something amazing that happened today:

_____

Day: _____   Date: __/__/___

1. Today I am *Grateful* for:

_____
_____
_____
_____
_____
_____

2. Something amazing that happened today:

_____

Day: _____   Date: __/__/___

1. Today I am *Grateful* for:

_____
_____
_____
_____
_____

2. Something amazing that happened today:

_____

The pleasure which we most rarely experience gives us
greatest delight. — Epictetus

Day: _____   Date: __/__/____

1. Today I am *Grateful* for:

_____
_____
_____
_____
_____
_____

2. Something amazing that happened today:

_____

Day: _____   Date: __/__/____

1. Today I am *Grateful* for:

_____
_____
_____
_____
_____
_____

2. Something amazing that happened today:

_____

Day: _____   Date: __/__/____

1. Today I am *Grateful* for:

_____
_____
_____
_____
_____
_____

2. Something amazing that happened today:

_____

Courtesies of a small and trivial character are the ones which strike deepest in the grateful and appreciating heart. — Henry Clay

Day: _____   Date: __/__/___

1. Today I am *Grateful* for:

_____
_____
_____
_____
_____

2. Something amazing that happened today:

_____

Day: _____   Date: __/__/___

1. Today I am *Grateful* for:

_____
_____
_____
_____
_____

2. Something amazing that happened today:

_____

Day: _____   Date: __/__/___

1. Today I am *Grateful* for:

_____
_____
_____
_____
_____

2. Something amazing that happened today:

_____

The essence of all beautiful art, all great art, is gratitude.
— Friedrich Nietzsche

Day: _____   Date: __/__/___

1. Today I am *Grateful* for:

_____
_____
_____
_____
_____
_____

2. Something amazing that happened today:

_____

Day: _____   Date: __/__/___

1. Today I am *Grateful* for:

_____
_____
_____
_____
_____

2. Something amazing that happened today:

_____

Day: _____   Date: __/__/___

1. Today I am *Grateful* for:

_____
_____
_____
_____
_____

2. Something amazing that happened today:

_____

Remember when life's path is steep to keep your mind even.
— Horace

Day: _____   Date: __/__/____

1. Today I am *Grateful* for:

_____

_____

_____

_____

_____

2. Something amazing that happened today:

_____

Day: _____   Date: __/__/____

1. Today I am *Grateful* for:

_____

_____

_____

_____

_____

2. Something amazing that happened today:

_____

Day: _____   Date: __/__/____

1. Today I am *Grateful* for:

_____

_____

_____

_____

_____

2. Something amazing that happened today:

_____

The real voyage of discovery consists not in seeking new
landscapes, but in having new eyes. — Marcel Proust

Day: _____   Date: __/__/____

1. Today I am *Grateful* for:

_____
_____
_____
_____
_____
_____
_____

2. Something amazing that happened today:

_____

Day: _____   Date: __/__/____

1. Today I am *Grateful* for:

_____
_____
_____
_____
_____
_____

2. Something amazing that happened today:

_____

Day: _____   Date: __/__/____

1. Today I am *Grateful* for:

_____
_____
_____
_____
_____

2. Something amazing that happened today:

_____

To forget oneself is to be happy.
— Robert Louis Stevenson

Day: _____   Date: __/__/____

1. Today I am *Grateful* for:

_____

_____

_____

_____

_____

_____

2. Something amazing that happened today:

_____

Day: _____   Date: __/__/____

1. Today I am *Grateful* for:

_____

_____

_____

_____

_____

2. Something amazing that happened today:

_____

Day: _____   Date: __/__/____

1. Today I am *Grateful* for:

_____

_____

_____

_____

_____

2. Something amazing that happened today:

_____

To have courage for whatever comes in life - everything
lies in that. — Saint Teresa of Avila

Day: _____   Date: __/__/____

1. Today I am *Grateful* for:
_____
_____
_____
_____
_____
_____

2. Something amazing that happened today:
_____

Day: _____   Date: __/__/____

1. Today I am *Grateful* for:
_____
_____
_____
_____
_____
_____

2. Something amazing that happened today:
_____

Day: _____   Date: __/__/____

1. Today I am *Grateful* for:
_____
_____
_____
_____
_____
_____

2. Something amazing that happened today:
_____

It is the heart always that sees, before the head can see.
— Thomas Carlyle

Day: _____   Date: __/__/___

1. Today I am *Grateful* for:

_____
_____
_____
_____
_____
_____

2. Something amazing that happened today:

_____

Day: _____   Date: __/__/___

1. Today I am *Grateful* for:

_____
_____
_____
_____
_____

2. Something amazing that happened today:

_____

Day: _____   Date: __/__/___

1. Today I am *Grateful* for:

_____
_____
_____
_____
_____

2. Something amazing that happened today:

_____

The thankful receiver bears a plentiful harvest.
— William Blake

Day: _____   Date: __/__/____

1. Today I am *Grateful* for:

_____
_____
_____
_____
_____
_____

2. Something amazing that happened today:

_____

Day: _____   Date: __/__/____

1. Today I am *Grateful* for:

_____
_____
_____
_____
_____
_____

2. Something amazing that happened today:

_____

Day: _____   Date: __/__/____

1. Today I am *Grateful* for:

_____
_____
_____
_____
_____

2. Something amazing that happened today:

_____

Be as you wish to seem.
— Socrates

Day: _____   Date: __/__/____

1. Today I am *Grateful* for:

_____

_____

_____

_____

_____

_____

2. Something amazing that happened today:

_____

Day: _____   Date: __/__/____

1. Today I am *Grateful* for:

_____

_____

_____

_____

_____

_____

2. Something amazing that happened today:

_____

Day: _____   Date: __/__/____

1. Today I am *Grateful* for:

_____

_____

_____

_____

_____

_____

2. Something amazing that happened today:

_____

The most certain sign of wisdom is cheerfulness.
— Michel de Montaigne

Day: _____   Date: __/__/____

1. Today I am *Grateful* for:

_____
_____
_____
_____
_____
_____

2. Something amazing that happened today:

_____

Day: _____   Date: __/__/____

1. Today I am *Grateful* for:

_____
_____
_____
_____
_____

2. Something amazing that happened today:

_____

Day: _____   Date: __/__/____

1. Today I am *Grateful* for:

_____
_____
_____
_____

2. Something amazing that happened today:

_____

Our life is what our thoughts make it.
— Marcus Aurelius

Day: _____   Date: __/__/____

1. Today I am *Grateful* for:

_____
_____
_____
_____
_____
_____

2. Something amazing that happened today:

_____

Day: _____   Date: __/__/____

1. Today I am *Grateful* for:

_____
_____
_____
_____
_____
_____

2. Something amazing that happened today:

_____

Day: _____   Date: __/__/____

1. Today I am *Grateful* for:

_____
_____
_____
_____
_____
_____

2. Something amazing that happened today:

_____

When unhappy, one doubts everything; when happy,
one doubts nothing. — Joseph Roux

Day: _____   Date: _/_/___

1. Today I am *Grateful* for:

_____
_____
_____
_____
_____
_____

2. Something amazing that happened today:

_____

Day: _____   Date: _/_/___

1. Today I am *Grateful* for:

_____
_____
_____
_____
_____
_____

2. Something amazing that happened today:

_____

Day: _____   Date: _/_/___

1. Today I am *Grateful* for:

_____
_____
_____
_____
_____
_____

2. Something amazing that happened today:

_____

What worries you, masters you.
— John Locke

Day: _____   Date: __/__/___

1. Today I am *Grateful* for:

_____
_____
_____
_____
_____

2. Something amazing that happened today:

_____

Day: _____   Date: __/__/___

1. Today I am *Grateful* for:

_____
_____
_____
_____
_____

2. Something amazing that happened today:

_____

Day: _____   Date: __/__/___

1. Today I am *Grateful* for:

_____
_____
_____
_____
_____

2. Something amazing that happened today:

_____

The art of being happy lies in the power of extracting
happiness from common things. — Henry Ward Beecher

Day: _____   Date: __/__/___

1. Today I am *Grateful* for:

_____

_____

_____

_____

_____

_____

2. Something amazing that happened today:

_____

Day: _____   Date: __/__/___

1. Today I am *Grateful* for:

_____

_____

_____

_____

_____

2. Something amazing that happened today:

_____

Day: _____   Date: __/__/___

1. Today I am *Grateful* for:

_____

_____

_____

_____

2. Something amazing that happened today:

_____

Blessed is the influence of one true, loving human soul
on another. — George Eliot

Day: _____   Date: _/_/___

1. Today I am *Grateful* for:

_____
_____
_____
_____
_____
_____

2. Something amazing that happened today:

_____

Day: _____   Date: _/_/___

1. Today I am *Grateful* for:

_____
_____
_____
_____
_____
_____

2. Something amazing that happened today:

_____

Day: _____   Date: _/_/___

1. Today I am *Grateful* for:

_____
_____
_____
_____
_____
_____

2. Something amazing that happened today:

_____

The best thing one can do when it's raining is to let it rain.
— Henry Wadsworth Longfellow

Day: _____   Date: __/__/___

1. Today I am *Grateful* for:

_____
_____
_____
_____
_____
_____

2. Something amazing that happened today:

_____

Day: _____   Date: __/__/___

1. Today I am *Grateful* for:

_____
_____
_____
_____
_____

2. Something amazing that happened today:

_____

Day: _____   Date: __/__/___

1. Today I am *Grateful* for:

_____
_____
_____
_____

2. Something amazing that happened today:

_____

Live your life as though your every act were to become
a universal law. — Immanuel Kant

Day: _____   Date: __/__/___

1. Today I am *Grateful* for:

_____

_____

_____

_____

_____

2. Something amazing that happened today:

_____

Day: _____   Date: __/__/___

1. Today I am *Grateful* for:

_____

_____

_____

_____

_____

2. Something amazing that happened today:

_____

Day: _____   Date: __/__/___

1. Today I am *Grateful* for:

_____

_____

_____

_____

_____

2. Something amazing that happened today:

_____

Never give up, for that is just the place and time that the tide will turn. — Harriet Beecher Stowe

Day: _____   Date: __/__/____

1. Today I am *Grateful* for:

_____
_____
_____
_____
_____
_____

2. Something amazing that happened today:

_____

Day: _____   Date: __/__/____

1. Today I am *Grateful* for:

_____
_____
_____
_____
_____

2. Something amazing that happened today:

_____

Day: _____   Date: __/__/____

1. Today I am *Grateful* for:

_____
_____
_____
_____
_____

2. Something amazing that happened today:

_____

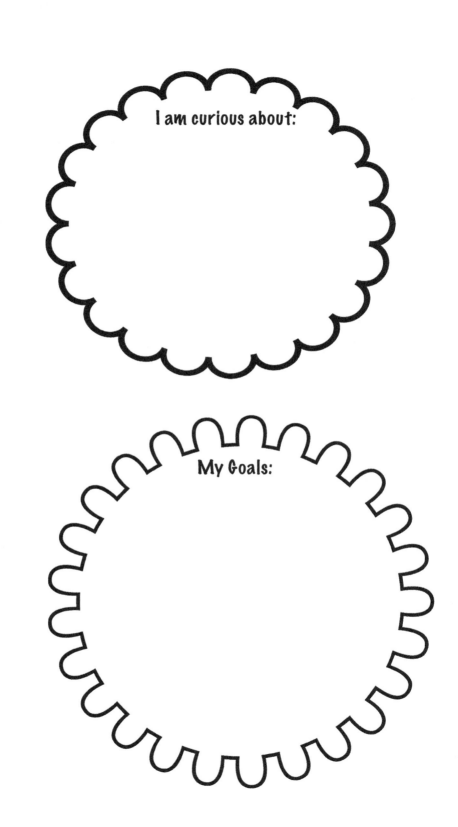

I am curious about:

My Goals:

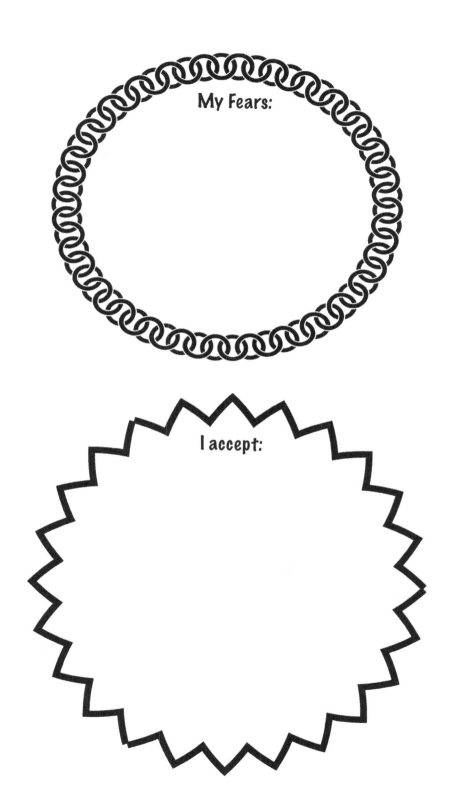

My Fears:

I accept:

The power of imagination makes us infinite.
— John Muir

Day: _____   Date: __/__/____

1. Today I am *Grateful* for:

_____
_____
_____
_____
_____
_____

2. Something amazing that happened today:

_____

Day: _____   Date: __/__/____

1. Today I am *Grateful* for:

_____
_____
_____
_____
_____
_____

2. Something amazing that happened today:

_____

Day: _____   Date: __/__/____

1. Today I am *Grateful* for:

_____
_____
_____
_____
_____
_____

2. Something amazing that happened today:

_____

Our will is always for our own good, but we do not
always see what that is. — Jean-Jacques Rousseau

Day: _____   Date: _/_/____

1. Today I am *Grateful* for:

_____
_____
_____
_____
_____
_____

2. Something amazing that happened today:

_____

Day: _____   Date: _/_/____

1. Today I am *Grateful* for:

_____
_____
_____
_____
_____

2. Something amazing that happened today:

_____

Day: _____   Date: _/_/____

1. Today I am *Grateful* for:

_____
_____
_____
_____
_____

2. Something amazing that happened today:

_____

To live is so startling it leaves little time for anything else.
— Emily Dickinson

Day: _____   Date: _/_/___

1. Today I am *Grateful* for:

_____
_____
_____
_____
_____

2. Something amazing that happened today:

_____

Day: _____   Date: _/_/___

1. Today I am *Grateful* for:

_____
_____
_____
_____
_____

2. Something amazing that happened today:

_____

Day: _____   Date: _/_/___

1. Today I am *Grateful* for:

_____
_____
_____
_____
_____

2. Something amazing that happened today:

_____

If you want the present to be different from the past,
study the past. — Baruch Spinoza

Day: _____   Date: __/__/____

1. Today I am *Grateful* for:

_____

_____

_____

_____

_____

_____

2. Something amazing that happened today:

_____

Day: _____   Date: __/__/____

1. Today I am *Grateful* for:

_____

_____

_____

_____

_____

_____

2. Something amazing that happened today:

_____

Day: _____   Date: __/__/____

1. Today I am *Grateful* for:

_____

_____

_____

_____

_____

_____

2. Something amazing that happened today:

_____

There are two ways of spreading light: to be the candle or the
mirror that reflects it. — Edith Wharton

Day: _____   Date: __/__/___

1. Today I am *Grateful* for:

_____

_____

_____

_____

_____

2. Something amazing that happened today:

_____

Day: _____   Date: __/__/___

1. Today I am *Grateful* for:

_____

_____

_____

_____

_____

2. Something amazing that happened today:

_____

Day: _____   Date: __/__/___

1. Today I am *Grateful* for:

_____

_____

_____

_____

_____

2. Something amazing that happened today:

_____

Gratitude is the sign of noble souls.
— Aesop Fables

Day: _____   Date: __/__/____

1. Today I am *Grateful* for:

_____

_____

_____

_____

_____

2. Something amazing that happened today:

_____

Day: _____   Date: __/__/____

1. Today I am *Grateful* for:

_____

_____

_____

_____

_____

2. Something amazing that happened today:

_____

Day: _____   Date: __/__/____

1. Today I am *Grateful* for:

_____

_____

_____

_____

_____

2. Something amazing that happened today:

_____

The energy of the mind is the essence of life.
— Aristotle

Day: _____   Date: _/_/____

1. Today I am *Grateful* for:

_____

_____

_____

_____

_____

_____

2. Something amazing that happened today:

_____

Day: _____   Date: _/_/____

1. Today I am *Grateful* for:

_____

_____

_____

_____

_____

_____

2. Something amazing that happened today:

_____

Day: _____   Date: _/_/____

1. Today I am *Grateful* for:

_____

_____

_____

_____

_____

_____

2. Something amazing that happened today:

_____

Tenderness is a virtue.
— Oliver Goldsmith

Day: _____   Date: __/__/___

1. Today I am *Grateful* for:
_____
_____
_____
_____
_____
_____

2. Something amazing that happened today:
_____

Day: _____   Date: __/__/___

1. Today I am *Grateful* for:
_____
_____
_____
_____
_____
_____

2. Something amazing that happened today:
_____

Day: _____   Date: __/__/___

1. Today I am *Grateful* for:
_____
_____
_____
_____
_____

2. Something amazing that happened today:
_____

We are born of love; Love is our mother.
— Rumi

Day: _____   Date: __/__/____

1. Today I am *Grateful* for:

_____

_____

_____

_____

_____

_____

2. Something amazing that happened today:

_____

Day: _____   Date: __/__/____

1. Today I am *Grateful* for:

_____

_____

_____

_____

_____

_____

2. Something amazing that happened today:

_____

Day: _____   Date: __/__/____

1. Today I am *Grateful* for:

_____

_____

_____

_____

_____

_____

2. Something amazing that happened today:

_____

It is great happiness to be praised of them who are most praiseworthy. — Philip Sidney

Day: _____   Date: __/__/____

1. Today I am *Grateful* for:
_____
_____
_____
_____
_____
_____

2. Something amazing that happened today:
_____

Day: _____   Date: __/__/____

1. Today I am *Grateful* for:
_____
_____
_____
_____
_____
_____

2. Something amazing that happened today:
_____

Day: _____   Date: __/__/____

1. Today I am *Grateful* for:
_____
_____
_____
_____
_____
_____

2. Something amazing that happened today:
_____

The best thinking has been done in solitude. The worst has been done in turmoil. — Thomas A. Edison

Day: _____   Date: __/__/___

1. Today I am *Grateful* for:

_____
_____
_____
_____
_____
_____

2. Something amazing that happened today:

_____

Day: _____   Date: __/__/___

1. Today I am *Grateful* for:

_____
_____
_____
_____
_____

2. Something amazing that happened today:

_____

Day: _____   Date: __/__/___

1. Today I am *Grateful* for:

_____
_____
_____
_____
_____

2. Something amazing that happened today:

_____

When the mind is thinking it is talking to itself.
— Plato

Day: _____   Date: __/__/____

1. Today I am *Grateful* for:

_____
_____
_____
_____
_____
_____

2. Something amazing that happened today:

_____

Day: _____   Date: __/__/____

1. Today I am *Grateful* for:

_____
_____
_____
_____
_____
_____

2. Something amazing that happened today:

_____

Day: _____   Date: __/__/____

1. Today I am *Grateful* for:

_____
_____
_____
_____
_____
_____

2. Something amazing that happened today:

_____

No man is an island, entire of itself; every man is a
piece of the continent. — John Donne

Day: _____   Date: __/__/____

1. Today I am *Grateful* for:

_____

_____

_____

_____

_____

2. Something amazing that happened today:

_____

Day: _____   Date: __/__/____

1. Today I am *Grateful* for:

_____

_____

_____

_____

_____

2. Something amazing that happened today:

_____

Day: _____   Date: __/__/____

1. Today I am *Grateful* for:

_____

_____

_____

_____

_____

2. Something amazing that happened today:

_____

What we obtain too cheap, we esteem too lightly; it is dearness only that gives everything its value. — Thomas Paine

Day: _____   Date: __/__/___

1. Today I am *Grateful* for:
_____
_____
_____
_____
_____
_____

2. Something amazing that happened today:
_____

Day: _____   Date: __/__/___

1. Today I am *Grateful* for:
_____
_____
_____
_____
_____
_____

2. Something amazing that happened today:
_____

Day: _____   Date: __/__/___

1. Today I am *Grateful* for:
_____
_____
_____
_____
_____

2. Something amazing that happened today:
_____

The best preparation for tomorrow is to do
today's work superbly well. — William Osler

Day: _____   Date: __/__/___

1. Today I am *Grateful* for:

_____
_____
_____
_____
_____
_____

2. Something amazing that happened today:

_____

Day: _____   Date: __/__/___

1. Today I am *Grateful* for:

_____
_____
_____
_____
_____

2. Something amazing that happened today:

_____

Day: _____   Date: __/__/___

1. Today I am *Grateful* for:

_____
_____
_____
_____
_____

2. Something amazing that happened today:

_____

You cannot do a kindness too soon, for you never know
how soon it will be too late. — Ralph Waldo Emerson

Day: _____   Date: __/__/____

1. Today I am *Grateful* for:

_____

_____

_____

_____

_____

2. Something amazing that happened today:

_____

Day: _____   Date: __/__/____

1. Today I am *Grateful* for:

_____

_____

_____

_____

_____

2. Something amazing that happened today:

_____

Day: _____   Date: __/__/____

1. Today I am *Grateful* for:

_____

_____

_____

_____

_____

2. Something amazing that happened today:

_____

Nothing ever becomes real till it is experienced.
— John Keats

Day: _____   Date: __/__/___

1. Today I am *Grateful* for:

_____

_____

_____

_____

_____

2. Something amazing that happened today:

_____

Day: _____   Date: __/__/___

1. Today I am *Grateful* for:

_____

_____

_____

_____

_____

2. Something amazing that happened today:

_____

Day: _____   Date: __/__/___

1. Today I am *Grateful* for:

_____

_____

_____

_____

_____

2. Something amazing that happened today:

_____

> In character, in manner, in style, in all things, the supreme
> excellence is simplicity. — Henry Wadsworth Longfellow

Day: _____   Date: __/__/___

1. Today I am *Grateful* for:

_____
_____
_____
_____
_____
_____

2. Something amazing that happened today:

_____

Day: _____   Date: __/__/___

1. Today I am *Grateful* for:

_____
_____
_____
_____
_____
_____

2. Something amazing that happened today:

_____

Day: _____   Date: __/__/___

1. Today I am *Grateful* for:

_____
_____
_____
_____
_____
_____

2. Something amazing that happened today:

_____

Wherever you go, go with all your heart.
— Confucius

Day: _____   Date: __/__/____

1. Today I am *Grateful* for:
_____
_____
_____
_____
_____
_____

2. Something amazing that happened today:
_____

Day: _____   Date: __/__/____

1. Today I am *Grateful* for:
_____
_____
_____
_____
_____
_____

2. Something amazing that happened today:
_____

Day: _____   Date: __/__/____

1. Today I am *Grateful* for:
_____
_____
_____
_____
_____
_____

2. Something amazing that happened today:
_____

To every action there is always opposed an equal reaction.
— Isaac Newton

Day: _____   Date: __/__/___

1. Today I am *Grateful* for:

_____

_____

_____

_____

_____

_____

2. Something amazing that happened today:

_____

Day: _____   Date: __/__/___

1. Today I am *Grateful* for:

_____

_____

_____

_____

_____

_____

2. Something amazing that happened today:

_____

Day: _____   Date: __/__/___

1. Today I am *Grateful* for:

_____

_____

_____

_____

_____

2. Something amazing that happened today:

_____

Draw something

I choose to allow:

I choose to receive:

A thousand words will not leave so deep an impression
as one deed. — Henrik Ibsen

Day: _____   Date: _/_/___

1. Today I am *Grateful* for:

_____

_____

_____

_____

_____

2. Something amazing that happened today:

_____

Day: _____   Date: _/_/___

1. Today I am *Grateful* for:

_____

_____

_____

_____

_____

2. Something amazing that happened today:

_____

Day: _____   Date: _/_/___

1. Today I am *Grateful* for:

_____

_____

_____

_____

_____

2. Something amazing that happened today:

_____

A contented mind is the greatest blessing a man can enjoy
in this world. — Joseph Addison

Day: _____   Date: __/__/___

1. Today I am *Grateful* for:

_____
_____
_____
_____
_____
_____

2. Something amazing that happened today:

_____

Day: _____   Date: __/__/___

1. Today I am *Grateful* for:

_____
_____
_____
_____
_____

2. Something amazing that happened today:

_____

Day: _____   Date: __/__/___

1. Today I am *Grateful* for:

_____
_____
_____
_____
_____

2. Something amazing that happened today:

_____

Real happiness is cheap enough, yet how dearly
we pay for its counterfeit. — Hosea Ballou

Day: _____   Date: __/__/___

1. Today I am *Grateful* for:

_____
_____
_____
_____
_____
_____

2. Something amazing that happened today:

_____

Day: _____   Date: __/__/___

1. Today I am *Grateful* for:

_____
_____
_____
_____
_____
_____

2. Something amazing that happened today:

_____

Day: _____   Date: __/__/___

1. Today I am *Grateful* for:

_____
_____
_____
_____
_____
_____

2. Something amazing that happened today:

_____

> Being deeply loved by someone gives you strength, while
> loving someone deeply gives you courage. — Lao Tzu

Day: _____   Date: __/__/____

1. Today I am *Grateful* for:

_____

_____

_____

_____

_____

_____

2. Something amazing that happened today:

_____

Day: _____   Date: __/__/____

1. Today I am *Grateful* for:

_____

_____

_____

_____

_____

_____

2. Something amazing that happened today:

_____

Day: _____   Date: __/__/____

1. Today I am *Grateful* for:

_____

_____

_____

_____

_____

_____

2. Something amazing that happened today:

_____

Truly, it is in darkness that one finds the light, so when we are in sorrow, then this light is nearest of all to us. — Meister Eckhart

Day: _____   Date: __/__/____

1. Today I am *Grateful* for:

_____
_____
_____
_____
_____
_____

2. Something amazing that happened today:

_____

Day: _____   Date: __/__/____

1. Today I am *Grateful* for:

_____
_____
_____
_____
_____
_____

2. Something amazing that happened today:

_____

Day: _____   Date: __/__/____

1. Today I am *Grateful* for:

_____
_____
_____
_____
_____
_____

2. Something amazing that happened today:

_____

Gratitude is not only the greatest of virtues, but the parent
of all the others. — Marcus Tullius Cicero

Day: _____   Date: __/__/___

1. Today I am *Grateful* for:

_____
_____
_____
_____
_____
_____

2. Something amazing that happened today:

_____

Day: _____   Date: __/__/___

1. Today I am *Grateful* for:

_____
_____
_____
_____
_____

2. Something amazing that happened today:

_____

Day: _____   Date: __/__/___

1. Today I am *Grateful* for:

_____
_____
_____
_____
_____

2. Something amazing that happened today:

_____

The sun does not shine for a few trees and flowers, but for the wide world's joy. — Henry Ward Beecher

Day: _____   Date: __/__/___

1. Today I am *Grateful* for:

_____
_____
_____
_____
_____
_____

2. Something amazing that happened today:

_____

Day: _____   Date: __/__/___

1. Today I am *Grateful* for:

_____
_____
_____
_____
_____

2. Something amazing that happened today:

_____

Day: _____   Date: __/__/___

1. Today I am *Grateful* for:

_____
_____
_____
_____
_____

2. Something amazing that happened today:

_____

How very little can be done under the spirit of fear.
— Florence Nightingale

Day: _____   Date: __/__/___

1. Today I am *Grateful* for:
_____
_____
_____
_____
_____
_____

2. Something amazing that happened today:
_____

Day: _____   Date: __/__/___

1. Today I am *Grateful* for:
_____
_____
_____
_____
_____
_____

2. Something amazing that happened today:
_____

Day: _____   Date: __/__/___

1. Today I am *Grateful* for:
_____
_____
_____
_____
_____
_____

2. Something amazing that happened today:
_____

To the artist there is never anything ugly in nature.
— Auguste Rodin

Day: _____   Date: __/__/____

1. Today I am *Grateful* for:

_____

_____

_____

_____

_____

2. Something amazing that happened today:

_____

Day: _____   Date: __/__/____

1. Today I am *Grateful* for:

_____

_____

_____

_____

_____

2. Something amazing that happened today:

_____

Day: _____   Date: __/__/____

1. Today I am *Grateful* for:

_____

_____

_____

_____

_____

2. Something amazing that happened today:

_____

True originality consists not in a new manner but in
a new vision. — Edith Wharton

Day: _____   Date: __/__/____

1. Today I am *Grateful* for:

_____

_____

_____

_____

_____

_____

2. Something amazing that happened today:

_____

Day: _____   Date: __/__/____

1. Today I am *Grateful* for:

_____

_____

_____

_____

_____

_____

2. Something amazing that happened today:

_____

Day: _____   Date: __/__/____

1. Today I am *Grateful* for:

_____

_____

_____

_____

_____

2. Something amazing that happened today:

_____

Who knows, the mind has the key to all things besides.
— Amos Bronson Alcott

Day: _____   Date: __/__/___

1. Today I am *Grateful* for:

_____
_____
_____
_____
_____
_____

2. Something amazing that happened today:

_____

Day: _____   Date: __/__/___

1. Today I am *Grateful* for:

_____
_____
_____
_____
_____
_____

2. Something amazing that happened today:

_____

Day: _____   Date: __/__/___

1. Today I am *Grateful* for:

_____
_____
_____
_____
_____
_____

2. Something amazing that happened today:

_____

No act of kindness, no matter how small,
is ever wasted. — Aesop

Day: _____   Date: __/__/___

1. Today I am *Grateful* for:

_____
_____
_____
_____
_____
_____

2. Something amazing that happened today:

_____

Day: _____   Date: __/__/___

1. Today I am *Grateful* for:

_____
_____
_____
_____
_____

2. Something amazing that happened today:

_____

Day: _____   Date: __/__/___

1. Today I am *Grateful* for:

_____
_____
_____
_____
_____

2. Something amazing that happened today:

_____

When words leave off, music begins.
— Heinrich Heine

Day: _____   Date: __/__/___

1. Today I am *Grateful* for:

_____
_____
_____
_____
_____
_____

2. Something amazing that happened today:

_____

Day: _____   Date: __/__/___

1. Today I am *Grateful* for:

_____
_____
_____
_____
_____

2. Something amazing that happened today:

_____

Day: _____   Date: __/__/___

1. Today I am *Grateful* for:

_____
_____
_____
_____
_____

2. Something amazing that happened today:

_____

A single grateful thought toward heaven is the most
perfect prayer. — Gotthold Ephraim Lessing

Day: _____   Date: __/__/___

1. Today I am *Grateful* for:

_____
_____
_____
_____
_____
_____

2. Something amazing that happened today:

_____

Day: _____   Date: __/__/___

1. Today I am *Grateful* for:

_____
_____
_____
_____
_____
_____

2. Something amazing that happened today:

_____

Day: _____   Date: __/__/___

1. Today I am *Grateful* for:

_____
_____
_____
_____
_____
_____

2. Something amazing that happened today:

_____

Positive anything is better than negative nothing.
— Elbert Hubbard

Day: _____   Date: __/__/____

1. Today I am *Grateful* for:

_____
_____
_____
_____
_____
_____

2. Something amazing that happened today:

_____

Day: _____   Date: __/__/____

1. Today I am *Grateful* for:

_____
_____
_____
_____
_____
_____

2. Something amazing that happened today:

_____

Day: _____   Date: __/__/____

1. Today I am *Grateful* for:

_____
_____
_____
_____
_____
_____

2. Something amazing that happened today:

_____

The purpose creates the machine.
— Arthur Young

Day: _____   Date: __/__/____

1. Today I am *Grateful* for:

_____
_____
_____
_____
_____
_____

2. Something amazing that happened today:

_____

Day: _____   Date: __/__/____

1. Today I am *Grateful* for:

_____
_____
_____
_____
_____
_____

2. Something amazing that happened today:

_____

Day: _____   Date: __/__/____

1. Today I am *Grateful* for:

_____
_____
_____
_____
_____

2. Something amazing that happened today:

_____

Saying and doing are two things.
— Matthew Henry

Day: _____   Date: __/__/____

1. Today I am *Grateful* for:

_____
_____
_____
_____
_____

2. Something amazing that happened today:

_____

Day: _____   Date: __/__/____

1. Today I am *Grateful* for:

_____
_____
_____
_____
_____

2. Something amazing that happened today:

_____

Day: _____   Date: __/__/____

1. Today I am *Grateful* for:

_____
_____
_____
_____
_____

2. Something amazing that happened today:

_____

Keep love in your heart. A life without it is like a sunless garden when the flowers are dead. — Oscar Wilde

Day: _____   Date: __/__/____

1. Today I am *Grateful* for:

_____
_____
_____
_____
_____
_____

2. Something amazing that happened today:

_____

Day: _____   Date: __/__/____

1. Today I am *Grateful* for:

_____
_____
_____
_____
_____
_____

2. Something amazing that happened today:

_____

Day: _____   Date: __/__/____

1. Today I am *Grateful* for:

_____
_____
_____
_____
_____
_____

2. Something amazing that happened today:

_____

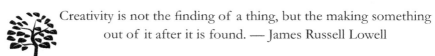

Creativity is not the finding of a thing, but the making something out of it after it is found. — James Russell Lowell

Day: _____   Date: __/__/____

1. Today I am *Grateful* for:

_____

_____

_____

_____

_____

_____

2. Something amazing that happened today:

_____

Day: _____   Date: __/__/____

1. Today I am *Grateful* for:

_____

_____

_____

_____

_____

_____

2. Something amazing that happened today:

_____

Day: _____   Date: __/__/____

1. Today I am *Grateful* for:

_____

_____

_____

_____

_____

2. Something amazing that happened today:

_____

Knowing is not enough; we must apply. Willing is not
enough; we must do. — Johann Wolfgang von Goethe

Day: _____   Date: __/__/___

1. Today I am *Grateful* for:

_____
_____
_____
_____
_____
_____

2. Something amazing that happened today:

_____

Day: _____   Date: __/__/___

1. Today I am *Grateful* for:

_____
_____
_____
_____
_____
_____

2. Something amazing that happened today:

_____

Day: _____   Date: __/__/___

1. Today I am *Grateful* for:

_____
_____
_____
_____
_____

2. Something amazing that happened today:

_____

I love:

I hate:

I want:

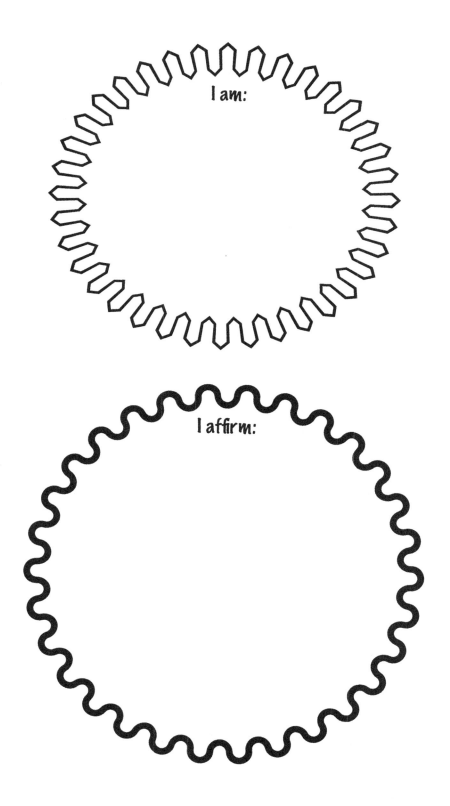

I am:

I affirm:

Painting from nature is not copying the object; it is realizing
one's sensations. — Paul Cezanne

Day: _____   Date: _/_/___

1. Today I am *Grateful* for:

_____
_____
_____
_____
_____

2. Something amazing that happened today:

_____

Day: _____   Date: _/_/___

1. Today I am *Grateful* for:

_____
_____
_____
_____
_____

2. Something amazing that happened today:

_____

Day: _____   Date: _/_/___

1. Today I am *Grateful* for:

_____
_____
_____
_____
_____

2. Something amazing that happened today:

_____

Day: _____   Date: __/__/____

1. Today I am *Grateful* for:

_____
_____
_____
_____
_____
_____

2. Something amazing that happened today:

_____

Day: _____   Date: __/__/____

1. Today I am *Grateful* for:

_____
_____
_____
_____
_____

2. Something amazing that happened today:

_____

Day: _____   Date: __/__/____

1. Today I am *Grateful* for:

_____
_____
_____
_____
_____

2. Something amazing that happened today:

_____

Our happiness depends on wisdom all the way.
— Sophocles

Day: _____   Date: __/__/___

1. Today I am *Grateful* for:

_____
_____
_____
_____
_____
_____

2. Something amazing that happened today:

_____

Day: _____   Date: __/__/___

1. Today I am *Grateful* for:

_____
_____
_____
_____
_____
_____

2. Something amazing that happened today:

_____

Day: _____   Date: __/__/___

1. Today I am *Grateful* for:

_____
_____
_____
_____
_____

2. Something amazing that happened today:

_____

If it were not for hopes, the heart would break.
— Thomas Fuller

Day: _____   Date: __/__/____

1. Today I am *Grateful* for:

_____
_____
_____
_____
_____
_____

2. Something amazing that happened today:

_____

Day: _____   Date: __/__/____

1. Today I am *Grateful* for:

_____
_____
_____
_____
_____

2. Something amazing that happened today:

_____

Day: _____   Date: __/__/____

1. Today I am *Grateful* for:

_____
_____
_____
_____
_____

2. Something amazing that happened today:

_____

Life is the flower for which love is the honey.
— Victor Hugo

Day: _____   Date: __/__/____

1. Today I am *Grateful* for:

_____

_____

_____

_____

_____

_____

2. Something amazing that happened today:

_____

Day: _____   Date: __/__/____

1. Today I am *Grateful* for:

_____

_____

_____

_____

_____

_____

2. Something amazing that happened today:

_____

Day: _____   Date: __/__/____

1. Today I am *Grateful* for:

_____

_____

_____

_____

_____

_____

2. Something amazing that happened today:

_____

The greatest weapon against stress is our ability to choose
one thought over another. — William James

Day: _____   Date: __/__/____

1. Today I am *Grateful* for:

_____
_____
_____
_____
_____
_____

2. Something amazing that happened today:

_____

Day: _____   Date: __/__/____

1. Today I am *Grateful* for:

_____
_____
_____
_____
_____
_____

2. Something amazing that happened today:

_____

Day: _____   Date: __/__/____

1. Today I am *Grateful* for:

_____
_____
_____
_____
_____

2. Something amazing that happened today:

_____

A gentle word, a kind look, a good-natured smile can work wonders and accomplish miracles. — William Hazlitt

Day: _____   Date: __/__/____

1. Today I am *Grateful* for:

_____

_____

_____

_____

_____

2. Something amazing that happened today:

_____

Day: _____   Date: __/__/____

1. Today I am *Grateful* for:

_____

_____

_____

_____

_____

2. Something amazing that happened today:

_____

Day: _____   Date: __/__/____

1. Today I am *Grateful* for:

_____

_____

_____

_____

_____

2. Something amazing that happened today:

_____

The things that we love tell us what we are.
— Thomas Aquinas

Day: _____   Date: __/__/___

1. Today I am *Grateful* for:

_____
_____
_____
_____
_____
_____
_____

2. Something amazing that happened today:

_____

Day: _____   Date: __/__/___

1. Today I am *Grateful* for:

_____
_____
_____
_____
_____

2. Something amazing that happened today:

_____

Day: _____   Date: __/__/___

1. Today I am *Grateful* for:

_____
_____
_____
_____
_____

2. Something amazing that happened today:

_____

Wisdom begins in wonder.
— Socrates

Day: _____   Date: __/__/____

1. Today I am *Grateful* for:

_____
_____
_____
_____
_____
_____

2. Something amazing that happened today:

_____

Day: _____   Date: __/__/____

1. Today I am *Grateful* for:

_____
_____
_____
_____
_____
_____

2. Something amazing that happened today:

_____

Day: _____   Date: __/__/____

1. Today I am *Grateful* for:

_____
_____
_____
_____
_____
_____

2. Something amazing that happened today:

_____

To seek the highest good is to live well.
— Saint Augustine

Day: _____   Date: __/__/___

1. Today I am *Grateful* for:

_____
_____
_____
_____
_____
_____

2. Something amazing that happened today:

_____

Day: _____   Date: __/__/___

1. Today I am *Grateful* for:

_____
_____
_____
_____
_____

2. Something amazing that happened today:

_____

Day: _____   Date: __/__/___

1. Today I am *Grateful* for:

_____
_____
_____
_____
_____

2. Something amazing that happened today:

_____

By experience we find out a short way by a long wandering.
— Roger Ascham

Day: _____   Date: __/__/____

1. Today I am *Grateful* for:

_____

_____

_____

_____

_____

_____

2. Something amazing that happened today:

_____

Day: _____   Date: __/__/____

1. Today I am *Grateful* for:

_____

_____

_____

_____

_____

_____

2. Something amazing that happened today:

_____

Day: _____   Date: __/__/____

1. Today I am *Grateful* for:

_____

_____

_____

_____

_____

_____

2. Something amazing that happened today:

_____

Out of nothing can come, and nothing can
become nothing. — Persius

Day: _____   Date: __/__/____

1. Today I am *Grateful* for:

_____
_____
_____
_____
_____
_____
_____

2. Something amazing that happened today:

_____

Day: _____   Date: __/__/____

1. Today I am *Grateful* for:

_____
_____
_____
_____
_____
_____
_____

2. Something amazing that happened today:

_____

Day: _____   Date: __/__/____

1. Today I am *Grateful* for:

_____
_____
_____
_____
_____
_____
_____

2. Something amazing that happened today:

_____

There are lots of people who mistake their imagination for their memory. — Josh Billings

Day: _____   Date: __/__/___

1. Today I am *Grateful* for:

_____
_____
_____
_____
_____
_____

2. Something amazing that happened today:

_____

Day: _____   Date: __/__/___

1. Today I am *Grateful* for:

_____
_____
_____
_____
_____
_____

2. Something amazing that happened today:

_____

Day: _____   Date: __/__/___

1. Today I am *Grateful* for:

_____
_____
_____
_____
_____
_____

2. Something amazing that happened today:

_____

Friends are the sunshine of life.
— John Hay

Day: _____   Date: __/__/____

1. Today I am *Grateful* for:

_____

_____

_____

_____

_____

_____

2. Something amazing that happened today:

_____

Day: _____   Date: __/__/____

1. Today I am *Grateful* for:

_____

_____

_____

_____

_____

2. Something amazing that happened today:

_____

Day: _____   Date: __/__/____

1. Today I am *Grateful* for:

_____

_____

_____

_____

_____

2. Something amazing that happened today:

_____

Be not simply good - be good for something.
— Henry David Thoreau

Day: _____   Date: __/__/____

1. Today I am *Grateful* for:

_____
_____
_____
_____
_____
_____

2. Something amazing that happened today:

_____

Day: _____   Date: __/__/____

1. Today I am *Grateful* for:

_____
_____
_____
_____
_____

2. Something amazing that happened today:

_____

Day: _____   Date: __/__/____

1. Today I am *Grateful* for:

_____
_____
_____
_____
_____

2. Something amazing that happened today:

_____

Grace is the beauty of form under the influence
of freedom. — Friedrich Schiller

Day: _____   Date: __/__/____

1. Today I am *Grateful* for:

_____

_____

_____

_____

_____

_____

2. Something amazing that happened today:

_____

Day: _____   Date: __/__/____

1. Today I am *Grateful* for:

_____

_____

_____

_____

_____

_____

2. Something amazing that happened today:

_____

Day: _____   Date: __/__/____

1. Today I am *Grateful* for:

_____

_____

_____

_____

_____

_____

2. Something amazing that happened today:

_____

Happiness is a virtue, not its reward.
— Baruch Spinoza

Day: _____   Date: __/__/___

1. Today I am *Grateful* for:

_____
_____
_____
_____
_____
_____

2. Something amazing that happened today:

_____

Day: _____   Date: __/__/___

1. Today I am *Grateful* for:

_____
_____
_____
_____
_____
_____

2. Something amazing that happened today:

_____

Day: _____   Date: __/__/___

1. Today I am *Grateful* for:

_____
_____
_____
_____
_____
_____

2. Something amazing that happened today:

_____

Happiness resides not in possessions, and not in gold,
happiness dwells in the soul. — Democritus

Day: _____   Date: __/__/___

1. Today I am *Grateful* for:

_____

_____

_____

_____

_____

_____

2. Something amazing that happened today:

_____

Day: _____   Date: __/__/___

1. Today I am *Grateful* for:

_____

_____

_____

_____

_____

_____

2. Something amazing that happened today:

_____

Day: _____   Date: __/__/___

1. Today I am *Grateful* for:

_____

_____

_____

_____

_____

2. Something amazing that happened today:

_____

Happiness depends upon ourselves.
— Aristotle

Day: _____   Date: __/__/____

1. Today I am *Grateful* for:

_____
_____
_____
_____
_____
_____

2. Something amazing that happened today:

_____

Day: _____   Date: __/__/____

1. Today I am *Grateful* for:

_____
_____
_____
_____
_____
_____

2. Something amazing that happened today:

_____

Day: _____   Date: __/__/____

1. Today I am *Grateful* for:

_____
_____
_____
_____
_____
_____

2. Something amazing that happened today:

_____

Happiness is not an ideal of reason, but of imagination.
— Immanuel Kant

Day: _____   Date: __/__/____

1. Today I am *Grateful* for:

_____

_____

_____

_____

_____

_____

2. Something amazing that happened today:

_____

Day: _____   Date: __/__/____

1. Today I am *Grateful* for:

_____

_____

_____

_____

_____

_____

2. Something amazing that happened today:

_____

Day: _____   Date: __/__/____

1. Today I am *Grateful* for:

_____

_____

_____

_____

_____

_____

2. Something amazing that happened today:

_____

What makes you laugh?

What are you passionate about?

What does an extraordinary life look like for you?

Success is dependent on effort.
— Sophocles

Day: _____   Date: __/__/____

1. Today I am *Grateful* for:

_____

_____

_____

_____

_____

_____

2. Something amazing that happened today:

_____

Day: _____   Date: __/__/____

1. Today I am *Grateful* for:

_____

_____

_____

_____

_____

_____

2. Something amazing that happened today:

_____

Day: _____   Date: __/__/____

1. Today I am *Grateful* for:

_____

_____

_____

_____

_____

_____

2. Something amazing that happened today:

_____

The risk of a wrong decision is preferable to the
terror of indecision. — Maimonides

Day: _____   Date: _/_/___

1. Today I am *Grateful* for:

_____
_____
_____
_____
_____

2. Something amazing that happened today:

_____

Day: _____   Date: _/_/___

1. Today I am *Grateful* for:

_____
_____
_____
_____
_____

2. Something amazing that happened today:

_____

Day: _____   Date: _/_/___

1. Today I am *Grateful* for:

_____
_____
_____
_____
_____

2. Something amazing that happened today:

_____

The way to know life is to love many things.
— Vincent Van Gogh

Day: _____   Date: __/__/____

1. Today I am *Grateful* for:

_____

_____

_____

_____

_____

_____

2. Something amazing that happened today:

_____

Day: _____   Date: __/__/____

1. Today I am *Grateful* for:

_____

_____

_____

_____

_____

_____

2. Something amazing that happened today:

_____

Day: _____   Date: __/__/____

1. Today I am *Grateful* for:

_____

_____

_____

_____

_____

_____

2. Something amazing that happened today:

_____

Persevere and preserve yourselves for
better circumstances. — Virgil

Day: _____   Date: __/__/___

1. Today I am *Grateful* for:

_____
_____
_____
_____
_____
_____

2. Something amazing that happened today:

_____

Day: _____   Date: __/__/___

1. Today I am *Grateful* for:

_____
_____
_____
_____
_____
_____

2. Something amazing that happened today:

_____

Day: _____   Date: __/__/___

1. Today I am *Grateful* for:

_____
_____
_____
_____
_____
_____

2. Something amazing that happened today:

_____

Beauty surrounds us, but usually we need to be
walking in a garden to know it. — Rumi

Day: _____   Date: __/__/___

1. Today I am *Grateful* for:

_____

_____

_____

_____

_____

2. Something amazing that happened today:

_____

Day: _____   Date: __/__/___

1. Today I am *Grateful* for:

_____

_____

_____

_____

_____

2. Something amazing that happened today:

_____

Day: _____   Date: __/__/___

1. Today I am *Grateful* for:

_____

_____

_____

_____

_____

2. Something amazing that happened today:

_____

By appreciation, we make excellence in others
our own property. — Voltaire

Day: _____   Date: __/__/___

1. Today I am *Grateful* for:

_____
_____
_____
_____
_____
_____

2. Something amazing that happened today:

_____

Day: _____   Date: __/__/___

1. Today I am *Grateful* for:

_____
_____
_____
_____
_____
_____

2. Something amazing that happened today:

_____

Day: _____   Date: __/__/___

1. Today I am *Grateful* for:

_____
_____
_____
_____
_____

2. Something amazing that happened today:

_____

Keep your face always toward the sunshine - and shadows
will fall behind you. — Walt Whitman

Day: _____   Date: __/__/___

1. Today I am *Grateful* for:

_____

_____

_____

_____

_____

_____

2. Something amazing that happened today:

_____

Day: _____   Date: __/__/___

1. Today I am *Grateful* for:

_____

_____

_____

_____

_____

_____

2. Something amazing that happened today:

_____

Day: _____   Date: __/__/___

1. Today I am *Grateful* for:

_____

_____

_____

_____

_____

2. Something amazing that happened today:

_____

This world is but a canvas to our imagination.
— Henry David Thoreau

Day: _____   Date: _/_/___

1. Today I am *Grateful* for:
_____
_____
_____
_____
_____
_____
_____

2. Something amazing that happened today:
_____

Day: _____   Date: _/_/___

1. Today I am *Grateful* for:
_____
_____
_____
_____
_____
_____
_____

2. Something amazing that happened today:
_____

Day: _____   Date: _/_/___

1. Today I am *Grateful* for:
_____
_____
_____
_____
_____
_____
_____

2. Something amazing that happened today:
_____

A picture is a poem without words.
— Horace

Day: _____   Date: __/__/___

1. Today I am *Grateful* for:

_____

_____

_____

_____

_____

_____

2. Something amazing that happened today:

_____

Day: _____   Date: __/__/___

1. Today I am *Grateful* for:

_____

_____

_____

_____

_____

_____

2. Something amazing that happened today:

_____

Day: _____   Date: __/__/___

1. Today I am *Grateful* for:

_____

_____

_____

_____

_____

_____

2. Something amazing that happened today:

_____

Tears of joy are like the summer rain drops pierced
by sunbeams. — Hosea Ballou

Day: _____   Date: __/__/___

1. Today I am *Grateful* for:

_____
_____
_____
_____
_____
_____

2. Something amazing that happened today:

_____

Day: _____   Date: __/__/___

1. Today I am *Grateful* for:

_____
_____
_____
_____
_____
_____

2. Something amazing that happened today:

_____

Day: _____   Date: __/__/___

1. Today I am *Grateful* for:

_____
_____
_____
_____
_____

2. Something amazing that happened today:

_____

In every walk with nature one receives far more than he seeks.
— John Muir

Day: _____   Date: _/_/____

1. Today I am *Grateful* for:

_____
_____
_____
_____
_____
_____

2. Something amazing that happened today:

_____

Day: _____   Date: _/_/____

1. Today I am *Grateful* for:

_____
_____
_____
_____
_____
_____

2. Something amazing that happened today:

_____

Day: _____   Date: _/_/____

1. Today I am *Grateful* for:

_____
_____
_____
_____
_____
_____

2. Something amazing that happened today:

_____

Rejoice in the things that are present; all else is
beyond thee. — Michel de Montaigne

Day: _____   Date: __/__/____

1. Today I am *Grateful* for:

_____

_____

_____

_____

_____

_____

_____

2. Something amazing that happened today:

_____

Day: _____   Date: __/__/____

1. Today I am *Grateful* for:

_____

_____

_____

_____

_____

_____

_____

2. Something amazing that happened today:

_____

Day: _____   Date: __/__/____

1. Today I am *Grateful* for:

_____

_____

_____

_____

_____

_____

2. Something amazing that happened today:

_____

Write it on your heart that every day is the best day in the year.
— Ralph Waldo Emerson

Day: _____   Date: __/__/___

1. Today I am *Grateful* for:

_____
_____
_____
_____
_____
_____

2. Something amazing that happened today:

_____

Day: _____   Date: __/__/___

1. Today I am *Grateful* for:

_____
_____
_____
_____
_____
_____

2. Something amazing that happened today:

_____

Day: _____   Date: __/__/___

1. Today I am *Grateful* for:

_____
_____
_____
_____
_____

2. Something amazing that happened today:

_____

We are here to add what we can to life, not to get what
we can from life. — William Osler

Day: _____   Date: __/__/___

1. Today I am *Grateful* for:

_____
_____
_____
_____
_____
_____

2. Something amazing that happened today:

_____

Day: _____   Date: __/__/___

1. Today I am *Grateful* for:

_____
_____
_____
_____
_____
_____

2. Something amazing that happened today:

_____

Day: _____   Date: __/__/___

1. Today I am *Grateful* for:

_____
_____
_____
_____
_____
_____

2. Something amazing that happened today:

_____

The pursuit, even of the best things, ought to be
calm and tranquil. — Marcus Tullius Cicero

Day: _____   Date: __/__/____

1. Today I am *Grateful* for:

_____

_____

_____

_____

_____

_____

2. Something amazing that happened today:

_____

Day: _____   Date: __/__/____

1. Today I am *Grateful* for:

_____

_____

_____

_____

_____

_____

2. Something amazing that happened today:

_____

Day: _____   Date: __/__/____

1. Today I am *Grateful* for:

_____

_____

_____

_____

_____

_____

2. Something amazing that happened today:

_____

Pleasure is none, if not diversified.
— John Donne

Day: _____   Date: __/__/____

1. Today I am *Grateful* for:

_____
_____
_____
_____
_____
_____

2. Something amazing that happened today:

_____

Day: _____   Date: __/__/____

1. Today I am *Grateful* for:

_____
_____
_____
_____
_____
_____

2. Something amazing that happened today:

_____

Day: _____   Date: __/__/____

1. Today I am *Grateful* for:

_____
_____
_____
_____
_____

2. Something amazing that happened today:

_____

Notes

Notes